HOW THE WEST LOST WORLD WAR III TO CHINA IN 2025

First published in United Kingdom in 2021 by Apollo Analysis Ltd,
The Mill, Blackdown Park, Haslemere, Surrey GU27 3BU

Red Lightning: How the West Lost World War III to China

Editor: Sarah Hudson
Design: Peter Dawson, www.gradedesign.com

ISBN 978-0-9567175-8-0

DAVID MURRIN

RED LIGHTNING

HOW THE WEST LOST WORLD WAR III TO CHINA IN 2025

APOLLO

This story is dedicated to all those who lost their lives or were injured either physically or mentally in the wars that were fought to protect Britain and the free world's democracy and freedoms.

Our Western society owes you a tremendous debt, one that we can only repay by learning from your sacrifice and preventing future wars through a national commitment to full-spectrum deterrence.

We must signal to aggressive nations who seek to further their expansionist objectives through conflict that we will defend with total commitment the gift of freedom that you bequeathed us.

CONTENTS

1.0
INTRODUCTION

Since the end of the Cold War the majority of the populations of the West have lived with the assumption that World War III (WWIII) would and could never take place. Because as Albert Einstein famously said, '*I know not with what weapons World War III will be fought, but World War IV will be fought with sticks and stones*'. However, what if an aggressive and expansive hegemonic challenger believed that the combination of the West's collapse in collective moral fibre and resolve, coupled with the use of powerful and decisive new weapons deployed en masse, could make WWIII winnable?

Unbeknown to the majority of Western politicians and their populations, the West has already embarked on its road to war with China, driven by the expansive ambitions of the Chinese Communist Party (CCP). This short fictional story is designed to catalyse increased awareness of the risks faced by the West from China. It is written from a future perspective looking back on World War III from a historical perspective.

The scenario is based on the theories of the rise and fall of Empires, described in my book *Breaking the Code of History*, published in 2009, a thesis that accurately predicted the evolution of China's hegemonic challenge, going back to its genesis in 2002. The thesis showed that China's rise in power would inevitably lead to an arms' race similar to that in the run up to 1914, whilst estimating the most probable timeframe for World War III as 2025–27. The 10-step path towards World War III is further explained in my soon-to-be-published book *The Road to Wars*.

In section 2.0 of this short story, I explain the strategic perspective that follows the path of events up to the present. I then extrapolate those events forward into 2025 to the point where China chooses to initiate a global conflict. I do this whilst integrating events with key cycles such as the prices of commodities, one which in the past has catalysed aggressors to initiate conflict, for example in 1914.

In the subsequent sections, I shift the story to examine the tactical consequences of China's opening stages of war, as experienced by two separate Royal Navy carrier groups. The first, based on the HMS *Prince of Wales* carrier group, operating in the Philippine Sea, deals with ships that have only iteratively evolved from those in service today. In stark contrast, the second carrier group, operating off the Iceland–Faroe Gap and based around HMS *Queen Elizabeth* and her escort group, has incorporated the majority of the new weapons that are in development today. What I seek to demonstrate is simple: the development and operational deployment of current evolutions in military capabilities will be critical if Britain and her allies are to effectively and safely deter inevitable Chinese aggression.

In the final section, 'The Endgame', I reveal the strategic consequences of China's successful war that allow it to dominate and subjugate the free nations of the world. A terrifying prospect, but one post the annexation of Hong Kong that no-one can deny, and one which would allow the CCP to eradicate global democracy and replace it with a hierarchical model of control and governance that would remain unchallenged for decades, if not centuries, just like the Roman Empire.

2.0
THE LONG PATH TO WORLD WAR III

2.1 THE ROAD TO WARS OF EXPANSION FOLLOWS A PREDICTABLE TRAJECTORY

History demonstrates that wars between nations are not accidental. Instead, they follow a clear road to war with defined escalatory signals along the way. Both World War I and World War II show such a path. The same is true of World War III. Its path began in 1996, when China enacted a 50-year plan with the end goal of dominating the world by 2048. Initially, the plan involved fooling Western powers into believing that China, if it were to be allowed into the global trading network of the World Trade Organization (WTO), would, in time, become more democratic. With such a carrot America enthusiastically sponsored China and invested in its economy, especially the manufacturing sector, as labour was so much cheaper than in the West. Fuelled by greed, Western companies soon picked up on this partnership and built new factories with local Chinese partners that, in time, became automated. In doing so, they quickly transferred their valuable intellectual property (IP) to Chinese hands. Chinese factories became the world's manufacturing base, undercutting all competition and destroying competitors. This created a serious manufacturing dependence on China in the decades to come.

The openness of Western society was exacerbated by the hubris of winning the Cold War. It offered an opportunity for the CCP to increase the flow of classified IP by enacting a huge long-term intelligence operation that involved cyber theft and traditional espionage. To succeed in this plan, the CCP mandated its state intelligence services to steal Western IP, wherever possible, to close the military–industrial gap.

2.2 THE RISE OF PRESIDENT XI

The administration of President Barack Obama was sadly led by a man who was initially blind to the magnitude of Chinese ambitions. President Xi Jinping, however, was (and is) the most effective, as well as ambitious, CCP leader since Chairman

Mao. Unlike Hitler, Stalin and Mao, Xi did not have psychological flaws that he projected onto his people. Rather, he had grown up experiencing the impact of losing the Leader's favour when his father, a junior minister, fell foul of Mao, casting a dark shadow on his family and his own upbringing, making his childhood extremely tough, but ultimately forging him in steel. The key lesson he learned was that to survive in the CCP, one had to be utterly ruthless and rise to the top. And even more importantly, that the higher the level of office one obtained, the safer one became. Thus, to Xi, power equalled survival.

Xi's personal ambition and desire to vindicate his family following his father's fall from grace within the CCP had taken him to the top of the party, where he sought to outdo Mao by controlling the People's Liberation Army Navy (PLAN) and the CCP simultaneously, whilst developing a second leadership culture around himself. He then further secured his position by creating a controlled state using new model intelligence-gathering systems and artificial intelligence (AI) to monitor and remove any dissenting voice in China's vast society. The results followed fast: Xi became the leader and controller of a population of 1.2 billion, ruling with an iron fist. The CCP, the PLAN and the Chinese people followed his directions without question.

However, if Xi was ambitious for himself, he was even more so for China, which he saw as being the rightful global hegemon. He extended his personal mantra for survival to China, making it ruthless and powerful too. He had learned valuable lessons from China's humiliations in the 19th century at the hands of Britain and other European powers, and from the Third Taiwan Straits Crisis, seeing that they were all a consequence of Chinese weakness and an inability to resist the Western powers. The parallels are clear: it was early life experiences that drove President Xi. On his watch, China would never experience the same humiliation as he and his family, but would rise and dominate the world.

Xi was a product of the Chinese system that, unlike the West, revered knowledge and academic capability within its leadership, as these were seen as essential elements to qualify for the role. Thus, he was an outstanding political strategist, demonstrating a clear grasp of the military dynamics that contained China's expansion. He devised strategies with his generals and close advisors to turn China's weaknesses into strengths. He was a student of Sun Tzu; he had studied the West in great detail, which through the hubris of declining empires, no Western politician had ever bothered to emulate. This was the West's cardinal error. If they had, they would have known that Xi was relentlessly hunting them down.

Two years into his premiership, Xi knew that the world had progressed from when the 50-year plan was conceived in 1996. The consequence of 9/11 was America embarking on a wild goose chase against an enemy that could never essentially change the American way of life, but which gave China a smokescreen behind which to operate, as attritional and unwinnable campaigns in Iraq and Afghanistan bled America dry, reducing its political will and undermining America's moral imperative to be a global hegemon.

By 2012, Xi realised that, although China was achieving the strategic aims of the 50-year plan well ahead of schedule, the rise of India, whose demographic size was comparable, meant that it could not afford to wait until 2048 to dominate the world. India presented the same strategic vice that Russia had inflicted on German ambitions in the run up to the two world wars, forcing Germany to attack before Russia became too militarily powerful. Similarly, China had been forced to move earlier than was ideal before India also became too powerful.

Xi had initially adhered to Deng Xiaoping's mantra of keeping China's intentions hidden until Beijing had the military power to match its ambitions. However, the weakness of the Obama administration offered an opportunity and Xi accelerated the 50-year plan and openly challenged America. This challenge was manifested by building the coral fortresses of the First Island Chain. Little did the West understand that this was, in effect, a replication of Hitler's strategy to occupy the Rhineland in March 1936 and build the Siegfried Line. In doing so, Hitler separated France from its allies to the south and east of Germany. Unable to come to each other's aid, the alliance soon crumbled and Hitler subsumed those same allies into his cause.

2.3 OBAMA'S WEAKNESS PAVED THE WAY FOR TRUMP'S EXPOSURE OF CHINESE INTENTIONS

Despite Obama's heralded pivot to contain China, by his second term he had belatedly realised how badly he had been duped by China and how much power America had ceded on every front. This paved the way for President Donald Trump and his slogan 'Make America Great Again', which resonated with the American public. But Trump had been singled out by President Vladimir Putin as a man who knew no limits – an extreme narcissist. As part of his grey zone war against America, Putin compromised Trump with loans to his business from subordinate oligarchs and then covertly manipulated the American electorate to help him win. Although not an agent of Putin's, at no time during his term did Trump say or do anything that acted against Russia, despite provocations that, under any other US president, should have resulted in extreme American responses. Importantly, there was another agenda for Putin; to covertly slow China's rise by awakening America to its threat. Trump, as he promised, soon set about exposing China as America's competitor through a trade war that, by the end of 2019, was injuring China's economic strategy and, most damagingly, polarising the Western world against China.

2.4 THE PERFECT TIMING OF A GLOBAL PANDEMIC FOR CHINA

To any astute observer, it is incredibly coincidental that the coronavirus pandemic spread from China at the height of the trade war. To this day, thanks to obstructions from the CCP, the origins of the pandemic are still unclear to the general public. This included the manipulation of the World Health Organization (WHO) investigation a year after the investigative team arrived in Wuhan as evidence was only allowed to flow through CCP officials to the team. Among Western intelligence services it became an accepted fact that the virus had originated from the Wuhan Institute of Virology, based on the clear adaptations of infectability that the virus demonstrated with respect to human cells, a behaviour that could never have happened via the zoonotic origins theory. The Wuhan laboratory had a long-documented bad safety record, so it was easy to believe that this had been another accident with horrendous consequences.

However, there has been, to this day, a sector within the intelligence services that believe that what was made to look accidental was actually an intentional release, timed to escape just before Chinese New Year into the Wuhan population, whose city had more foreign workers than any other in China. The timing and location of the outbreak could not have been more perfect to initiate a global pandemic. Xi could have made the simple calculation that China's large population, central control, prior experience with SARS 1 and Confucian social order would have greater anti-entropy, compared to the West, to combat the pandemic. In this he was proved to be absolutely correct, as China's economy forged ahead, while the West's floundered into recession and depression.

Another theory was that in August 2019 a benign version of the virus, designed to inoculate the population, had been released and caused the largest flu epidemic in China up to Christmas, traces of which were found in Western sewage samples as early as September 2019. Either way, whether the virus was released intentionally or accidentally, the CCP maximised the conditions that allowed it to spread through the West in what amounted to an act of war. This included using their control of the WHO to slow any global warning about its impending spread and severity.

Liberal policies in Western democracies caused hesitancy before restrictions on personal freedoms were imposed. Combined with poor leadership responses, this guaranteed that the pandemic would spread in a sequence of multi-strain waves that defied national vaccination programmes. Ultimately, this separated countries into two groups: those able to vaccinate their populations, and those that became breeding grounds for new variants and mutations, which then further isolated them from the world.

Despite attempts by governments to print money and use debt to support their collapsing economies, the effects of lockdown sent Western nations into the deepest depression in modern history. This contrasted with China's economy which, through various strategies, maintained its positive growth (albeit at a lesser degree). This economic disparity swiftly closed the Sino-American GDP gap and made it more likely that China would become the world's most powerful economy by 2023. Moreover, as the depression deepened, a Western debt crisis unfolded by the end of 2021.

This was the inevitable product of America's increasing debt burden, lack of growth and decline as a hegemony, impacted by a sudden upswing in inflation driven by significant commodity price increases from late 2021. The result was higher interest rates and stagflation, which made American and European debt levels untenable. The ensuing economic fallout left Western economies in a similar state as they had experienced in the early 1930s.

2.5 XI INITIATES CHINA'S FIVE-YEAR PLAN

After Germany invaded the Rhineland in 1936, Hitler initiated his four-year plan. This was a strategy by which Germany's economy was transformed into an internally driven consumer economy. As part of this process, Germany stockpiled resources and prevented the Royal Navy from enacting a crippling blockade, similar to World War I, which finally forced Germany to agree to an armistice and then in 1919 to sign the Versailles Treaty. The downside of this plan was that by 1940 Hitler had to go to war or Germany would have been bankrupt. This was a critical dynamic which Western leaders, who advocated appeasement, failed to understand until it was too late.

Similarly, in mid-2020, China switched its economic strategy from an export-driven economy to one akin to Germany's post-1936. It became self-contained, fuelled by its own consumers and supported by an expanding military-industrial complex, building weapons of war. Also similar to Germany in 1936, China in 2020 began stockpiling natural resources, especially oil and basic metals, but also soya and other grains that China was reliant on through imports. This strategy was to send resource prices sky-high over the next five years with the greatest stockpiling plan in economic history. Notably, China also used its 80% global monopoly in mining and processing of rare earth metals as an economic weapon to retaliate over the chip wars, forcing the West into an emergency substitution strategy of resourcing from and refining outside China.

By the end of 2020, Trump lost the presidential election due to the economic impact of the pandemic and his failed policy response, which further exacerbated the wealth divide across America. This gave Joe Biden's wealth distribution policies more traction within the electorate and gained him ultimate victory. This was a significant dividend for Xi's pandemic plan. The added bonus was that by the time Biden was inaugurated in January 2021 Trump had sent a wrecking ball through the structure of American democracy with his encouragement of the Capitol Hill riot. Consequently, the political chaos increasingly replicated the energy of a civil war that lasted through Biden's administration. This political crisis was further compounded by the accelerating impact of the pandemic's second wave in mid-2021 that choked the economy and sent the markets into free fall.

One of the last acts of the Trump administration was to repudiate the One China policy and recognise Taiwan as an independent democracy, lifting all self-imposed diplomatic restrictions. Initially, this went unnoticed in the West. To the CCP, however, this was a similar red line as the Western-catalysed revolution in Ukraine had been to Putin.

2.6 XI ANNEXES TAIWAN

Using the pandemic chaos in America, in late 2021 China commenced an annexation of Taiwan. Initially, they used covert insurgent forces that decapitated the nation's leadership by killing the prime minister as well as the top civilian and military leaders. At the same time, China shut down 70% of Taiwan's defensive capability with a massive cyber-attack. During the chaos, a group of pro-China Taiwanese politicians made a formal request for help from the CCP to quell what it described as civil chaos.

The PLAN, on standby for what had been a so-called 'scheduled amphibious exercise' on a nearby island, were swiftly diverted and the annexation and invasion of Taiwan was over in 48 hours, well before the West could react. Faced with the possibility of potentially huge losses in trying to recapture Taiwan at a time of domestic chaos, America chose to do nothing. The annexation gave China access to state-of-the-art microchip production that had been denied to it by the Trump chips embargo. Most of all, it had strengthened China's First Island Chain and placed South

Korea next in the queue at high risk of an invasion from North Korea, supported by the PLAN. This was the final stepping-stone for an invasion of Japan in the years ahead.

2.7 THE SECOND IRON CURTAIN SLAMMED SHUT

The second Iron Curtain had completed its fall. This then divided the world and ushered in the acceleration of the fourth great industrial arms' race between China and Russia versus the West and its Pacific allies. Britain, having experienced the CCP's annexation of Hong Kong and subsequent brutal subjugation of democracy, combined with strong intelligence evidence (that remained classified) that the release of the Covid-19 virus had been intentional, acted decisively by leading the denunciation of China. America swiftly followed in its condemnation of Chinese aggression. Notably, the EU had a more muted response as it sought to preserve trade ties at any cost. Britain once more joined America in a common cause and enacted a new major rearmament programme, spending £180 billion per year. Britain justified this investment by rightly claiming it stimulated domestic growth and helped to build new trade relationships with its allies.

2.8 AMERICA AND ITS ALLIES BELATEDLY INCREASE DEFENCE SPENDING

President Biden was finally forced to accelerate US defence spending to 10% of GDP as part of his New Deal economic plan, and to reverse the decline of the US Navy, which Trump had promised to reverse at the start of his presidency with a plan to expand the 285-ship into a 355-ship Navy by 2030. However, his resources were diverted to the Mexican Wall, thus forcing the US Navy to announce a reduced ship plan days before Trump's departure from the White House. This projected that over the next five years the Navy would retire over 30 major combat units, including a carrier, cruisers and destroyers, to be replaced by 179 new smaller manned and robotic missile corvettes, 40 robotic submarines, 27 small amphibious landing ships and 18 small logistic ships, to take the total force to 600 combat units.

However, this effective Navy force reduction was a key signal to Xi, similar to the UK withdrawal of the ice patrol ship, HMS *Endurance*, that catalysed Argentina into invading the Falkland Islands. This message of American weakness encouraged Xi's annexation of Taiwan.

2.9 THE FORMATION OF THE PACIFIC TREATY ORGANISATION

Whilst Biden was unable to deter Chinese aggression through the demonstration of believable intention, he was an old-school American politician who understood the power of alliances. Along with Japan, he swiftly encouraged the formalisation of what was loosely known as the Quad into the Pacific Treaty Organisation (PTO), along similar lines as the formation of NATO. This comprised the Quad nations of America, Japan, Australia and India, plus the UK, South Korea and New Zealand. The alliance's headquarters were based at Pearl Harbor and led by an American admiral with a Japanese admiral as second-in-command. Naval task groups comprised multinational forces, based on a new flexible force doctrine introduced by the US Navy in 2021, that would take years to develop into an effective doctrine, harnessing networked combat information and allowing increased distance between combat units and larger areas of direct control. The warships of all the PTO members, except perhaps India, had been designed for mutual combat operations and, as such, the naval aspect of the PTO represented a very powerful enhancement of maritime combat capability available to contain China.

2.10 BIDEN'S FAILED RUSSIA STRATEGY SAVED BY REVOLUTION

As if the strategic situation could not get worse, from the beginning of his presidency Biden had failed to understand that seducing Russia back into the Western fold, however unpalatable, was critical. On a strategic level a US–Russia alliance would have surrounded China and denied it access to huge Russian resources overland, away from the Chinese navy and any potential blockade. To do so, Biden would have needed to place his own outrage at the injustice of Russia interfering in America's election below the strategic imperative of surrounding China. However, Biden chose otherwise. With increasingly belligerent rhetoric he sought to present strength to the world and so was in the process of pushing Russia firmly into the hands of China. Then fate intervened.

During the Cold War, the USSR was essentially a commodity nation facing a consumer-based West. Thus, at the peak of the last commodity cycle in 1975, it was inevitable that the USSR's economy translated into apparent ideological and military influence that appeared stronger than the West. However, by the end of the 1980s, the commodity cycle was in decline and that advantage had reversed to the point of economic collapse, ultimately causing the Berlin Wall to come down. Similarly, in 2021, the effect of a 10-year decline in commodity prices, in addition to the significant fiscal drag of the Putin kleptocracy, had significantly lowered living standards. This was then further compounded by the economic impact of the pandemic, which sent Russia's economy into a depression.

In late 2021, one of the consequences of the depression was a popular uprising in support of Alexei Navalny, Putin's extremely courageous, determined and most outspoken critic. The uprising was triggered after Navalny's arrest on his return to Russia after being poisoned by the nerve agent Novichok. However, Navalny was not alone, as he received covert support from the CIA and other Western intelligence services, who responded to Putin's meddling in Western democracies with interest. The result was that Putin was swept aside and Russia suddenly shifted to a pro-West nation, severing its ties with China. In one great geopolitical shift, China became surrounded and contained and its access to natural resources and especially liquefied natural gas became potentially vulnerable.

The Third Russian Revolution had averted the prospect of China and Russia forming a powerful economic and military alliance. However, in a last moment of spite against the West, Putin shared Russia's advanced military technology with China. This included hypersonic missiles and, most damagingly for the West, submarine technology. In this area, until now, the PLAN had been decades behind, but with this new knowledge the Chinese began building nuclear-powered, ballistic missile-carrying submarines (SSBNs) and nuclear-powered general-purpose attack submarines (SSNs) that were comparable to those of the West at rates echoing WWII US shipbuilding programmes. By 2025, 60 new SSNs and five SSBNs had entered PLAN active service, as part of the largest submarine fleet in the world. The consequence was clear: suddenly, American and allied submarine forces were globally under immense pressure. The only counter to this disastrous technology transfer was that under President Navalny, Russia soon joined the PTO, completing the encirclement of China, significantly pushing back Xi's plans for Chinese domination by adding the Russian navy's very significant and capable submarine force to the balance of power against China.

2.11 THE EVOLUTION OF AMERICAN POLITICS

President Biden passed away in 2022 after contracting Covid-19 in the fifth wave of the pandemic. The virus had mutated multiple times and every time a population had been vaccinated they became infected with new variants from countries that had not been vaccinated. His death finally triggered a global vaccination alliance, led by President Kamala Harris, that led to a coordinated global programme to inoculate the entire human population within a four-month period, thus killing off the possibility of any further mutation. It was the greatest collective human endeavour in history and showed what humanity could do when aligned to a common cause. However, Harris, much like former German Chancellor Angela Merkel, could not see the clear and present danger the PLAN presented to America. She failed to match the CCP's ever-escalating military production so that by the 2024 US presidential election China had become the biggest issue.

Indeed, by 2023 the threat had driven the Republican Party to revolution that drove out the Trumpites and replaced them with a new younger Republican movement. They elected a former US Navy admiral to lead the party, and in November 2024, President T K James was elected to office. James set about accelerating the US arms' race, but it proved to be too little too late. Xi's private memoirs also attest to his recognition that with the highly capable James becoming president, the timing of his planned attack was reaffirmed as 2025. If it had been left any longer, China's hard-won advantages might have soon been eroded by the US and the PTO.

2.12 COMMODITY PRICES INCREASE BEAT OF THE DRUMS OF WAR

Meanwhile, during the intervening years, as the price of commodities soared, new Asian Cold War tensions continued to build between the ascendant PTO and China. This was purely due to the two great economies on either side of the Iron Curtain consuming ever-greater amounts of materials for their military programmes. There were two main moments of heightened tension, where both sides reached the brink of war. In mid-2022, a Chinese cyber-attack on South Korea compromised American power stations and, in 2024, sent one of its nuclear reactors into meltdown. However, like the two previous world wars, it was always going to be the aggressor making the first move, having finessed the very best moment to strike.

Meanwhile, the hidden drumbeat of the commodity cycle, with its rocketing prices, triggered Xi's strategy. As prices rose, Russia, led by Navalny, became increasingly confident and assertive against China. More than once Navalny threatened to withhold its gas from China if Xi did not acquiesce to his demand that China back down from its aggression.

Gas piped overland from Russia reduced China's vulnerability to a maritime supply blockade. However, the high prices that Russia could charge meant it now had a hold over China. By 2024, Xi knew that it was time for China to take ownership of this critical resource chain. Attacking Russia coincided with the five-year plan, launched in 2020 as the pandemic spread around the world, to prepare for war with the West. That plan successfully shifted China from an export-driven economy to an internally fuelled consumer society, one in which China's manufacturing base had been used to build warships and ballistic missiles at a rate that had shocked the world, surpassing America's own WWII production rate.

The reality was that, by 2025, the PTO was fast losing the arms' race, both in terms of numbers and capability. Whilst Western leaders had become increasingly alarmed at China's military expansion, like their predecessors in the run up to 1914 and 1939 they had done too little too late to deter their aggression. This situation had been compounded by the economic weakness and markets crisis that had followed as a consequence of the response to the coronavirus pandemic.

Thus it was that on 8 August 2025, President Xi stared down the table at his Chiefs of the People's Liberation Army (PLA) and the PLAN and quietly gave the order to execute his surprise attack on Russia and the naval forces of the PTO, an operation which has since become known as *Red Lightning*.

3.0
XI'S SURPRISE ATTACK STARTS WORLD WAR III

3.1 CHINA'S WAR PLANNING

Xi and his most senior officers had been secretly planning for war since the beginning of the 2020 pandemic but only agreed their final strategy in early 2024.

The first defence for any nation against attack has always been its intelligence services, and the West has always had excellent capabilities. Therefore, the first step in a workable Chinese plan had to be to achieve total surprise from what appeared to be a cold start (in other words, without any detectable conventional force build-up). So, a mission critical part of the strategy had been the construction of a 20,000-strong PLA Chinese mobile rocket force, which Central Command could rapidly deploy, automatically targeting and launching at key objectives. Another crucial aspect was the expansion of the PLA Airborne Corps from 30,000 in 2020 to 300,000 in 2025. Not only had this force expanded tenfold, but it was designed to operate as a rapid reaction force that could deploy anywhere inside a 2,000-mile radius from the Chinese border.

Furthermore, it had been restructured to emulate the US Marine Corps' shift to light mobile forces, equipped with a high density of missile systems, simultaneously deployed with mass drone AI-controlled swarms, based around small stealthy sensor drones, larger stealthy mother drones, and numerous small suicide drones with anti-personnel and anti-armour capabilities. This new combat structure represented a highly potent strike force, where a PLA company could deploy the same combat power as a traditional armoured battle group. A third of these forces were always maintained at two-hour readiness, with the second third on 24 hours' notice and the last third at 10 days' notice. This rapid reaction capability from a cold start was never fully appreciated by PTO forces.

Most importantly, Xi's plan was designed to operate below the nuclear threshold of Western and Russian responses. He would win the war by conventional means in a swift and powerful strike, lasting just three days. Although there were three main components to the masterplan, *Red Lightning* was the core of the attack and, as such, Xi referred to the whole operation by this code name.

3.2 OPERATION *RED LIGHTNING*

Red Lightning was a simultaneous attack on all PTO (Western, Quad and Russian) warships across the globe by a massed 10,000-strong anti-ship ballistic missile attack. It was designed to clear the oceans of all enemy warships. This would pave the way for control of the oceans by the PLAN, the largest blue-water navy in the world. It was preceded by nuclear electromagnetic pulse (EMP) detonations in space to remove all satellites in orbit, including Chinese ones, which would then swiftly be replaced by a new wave of satellites, launched by the PLAN. This denied control of the high ground to the West and aimed to give ultimate control of it to the PLA.

3.3 OPERATION *RED CLOUD*

Red Cloud was the global cyber-attack on key political and military installations of target nations, designed to confuse and confound any coherent response. In addition, the operation included disinformation passed to Western sources that US warships had made an unprovoked attack and launched missiles against a PLAN carrier force operating south of the Taiwan Straits. Not only did this confuse the initial Western response, but most importantly, via the state media services, it mobilised Chinese public opinion into a wave of righteous indignation. The CCP had spent years developing the modern tools of communication and social manipulation, complete with a narrative that would ensure they had complete control over their own population in the conflict ahead. In contrast, the freedoms of the Western press had allowed the CCP to initiate programmes of control and interference that would be used to undermine the resolve of the PTO nations at critical points in the conflict. This included the transmission of last-minute target imagery onto Western feeds from warheads as they impacted their targets. Patched into a mosaic, this provided dramatic imagery, illustrating the success of their strikes.

3.4 OPERATION *RED WAVE*

Red Wave was a simultaneous surprise airborne assault, driving north into Siberian Russia and as far west as the Urals. The objective was to capture the critical resources that China needed to sustain its economy. These resources were judged to be so vital that Xi was prepared to risk a full ground assault on Russia to secure them. It was preceded by a strike from 1,000 DF-21 missiles targeting the Russian air defence systems which were swiftly neutralised by a cyber worm that had lain dormant for 18 months after a successful covert operation to insert it into the Russian system. This allowed the tactical strike planes assigned to the rapid reaction forces to hard kill the air defence systems and defeat any fighter formations, whilst allowing combat formations to be deployed by parachute directly onto key targets in Russia. All combat drops were preceded by drone swarms to first secure the drop zones.

All three of the above operations were meticulously prepared in secret and, up until the moments when the attacks were launched, there were no intelligence signals to indicate their impending strike.

3.5 THE ATTACK COMMENCES

At 03.45 GMT on 8 August 2025 Xi gave his senior officers gathered around the table a signal command: 'Execute Strike'. At 04.00 Operation *Red Cloud* spread chaos across the world's military and communications networks. Simultaneously, the PLAN alert status airborne forces were spun up and given their orders for Operation *Red Wave* and a mission go at 06.00. At the same time 25 DF-31s arched into the air from the Chinese mainland and in a matter of minutes they had reached an altitude of between 80 and 300km, forming a starburst pattern that enveloped the globe. They exploded in blinding nuclear flashes to create a directional EMP blast pointing spacewards that destroyed all satellites in orbit, blinding America and its allies to what was to follow.

Seconds later, waves of massed PLA Dongfeng missiles took to the skies from the Chinese mainland. These consisted of thousands of short-range Dongfeng DF-21s (2,500km), medium-range DF-26s (5,000km), long-range DF-31s (8,000km+) and super long-range DF-41s (12,000–15,000km).

America's newly deployed quantum radars quickly picked up the launches, swiftly starting to calculate trajectories and likely targets. Western forces quickly went to DEFCON 1, but the answer came swiftly that this was not a classic all-out nuclear attack, despite some 10,000 missiles in the air. Instead, all were focused at PTO targets located in harbours, seas and oceans, with the key concentration on locations where PTO battle groups and warships were operating to constrict the PLAN to within the Second Island Chain, or where they were prevented access into the North Atlantic by the now open North Passage, which had become free of ice over the past few years as climate change continued to accelerate faster than any scientific group had predicted.

4.0
RED LIGHTNING DESCENDS ON THE WESTERN PACIFIC

4.1 PTO NAVAL FORCE DISPOSITIONS

By 2025 the PTO had four carrier battle groups continuously at sea on PLAN containment duties in the Western Pacific and Indian Ocean. This included three groups each based around a US Navy super carrier supplemented by a Royal Navy carrier group from 2021 onwards, as Britain post-Brexit rapidly moved to a new global maritime world view that shifted its trading focus from an economically moribund EU to a more dynamic Asia. With 60% of global maritime trade passing through Asia, of which a third was passing through the South China Seas, the maintenance of open sea lanes became of international strategic importance.

4.2 HMS *PRINCE OF WALES* CARRIER GROUP: PHILIPPINE SEA

Thus, on 8 August 2025, cruising off the Philippine Sea between Taiwan and Japan, the powerful HMS *Prince of Wales* carrier group was part of a chain comprising three other US Navy carrier groups to contain any Chinese breakout from the First Island Chain. Such operations had become standard due to a build-up of tension since 2024. The group consisted of two Type 45 batch I air defence destroyers and three Type 26 anti-submarine warfare (ASW) frigates: HMS *Glasgow*, HMS *Birmingham* and HMS *Newcastle*. These were acting as the inner screen around 8km from the carrier and its supply ships. Although originally designated as the Type 26 *City*-class, the initial weapons suit was deemed too lightly armed and were upgraded to a similar standard as the Canadian variants. Similarly, the two Type 45 destroyers, HMS *Dragon* and HMS *Defender*, had been upgraded with enhanced anti-ballistic missile (ABM) radars and ABM-capable sea vipers with added layers of close protection from 40mm chain guns (range 10,000m) to supplement the Phalanx 20mm close-in weapon systems (CIWS) (range 1,500m). Alongside these chain guns sat new high-energy lasers with an effective range of 10km. These destroyers were supported by one USS

Arleigh Burke Flight III-class ABM destroyer and the 10,000-tonne ballistic missile defence Japanese super destroyer JS *Maya* equipped with then new SPY-7 and SM3 and SM6 missiles. Both were operating at 30km from the carrier. The subsea screen was operating up to 80km from the carrier and was provided by two UK *Astute*-class submarines, HMS *Astute* and HMS *Audacious*, supported by the *Virginia*-class attack boat USS *California* with its electromagnetic recognition identification system which greatly enhanced the detection of low acoustic signature targets, such as the most recent PLAN submarines. The older (and slightly less capable) *Los Angeles*-class, the USS *Providence*, comprised the fourth SSN in the carrier group.

4.3 PEARL HARBOR ALL OVER AGAIN

The attack caught the Prince of Wales carrier group completely by surprise. Whilst they, like all other PTO naval forces, had been on a high state of alert, the size and severity of the attack was immense. The first the carrier group knew of any danger was from the effects of the EMP above it. Although directed predominantly skywards, it momentarily interrupted their electronic systems. Next, the long-range S1850m radar on the Prince of Wales, positioned higher than the radars of her escorts, picked up the PLA missile launches. This state-of-the-art radar system had been upgraded to the specification of the SMART-L-EWC (early-warning capability) and was capable of picking up ballistic missiles over 3,000km away as they launched. The information fed into the fleet's combat network. High above, at 35,000ft, the two patrolling F35Bs, armed with the new and very powerful 25MW air-to-air lasers, had been disabled by the effects of the EMP and were struggling to stay airborne as they made an emergency landing on the carrier. However, a new replacement combat air patrol was quickly launched within two minutes, taking a further 60 seconds to climb to 35,000ft above the group. They were positioned between the incoming missiles and the fleet, able to track the missiles and pass the data back to the fleet network. This enhanced the tactical picture the carrier group now faced.

As the fleet's multiple radars picked through the mass of missiles, they locked onto some 300 warheads aimed at the carrier group. The first ships in the fleet to fire were the US and Japanese destroyers who simultaneously launched their long-range SM6s, designed to intercept during the mid-course section of the incoming DF-21s and DF-26s. This was the easiest point of interception before the hypersonic warhead could detach and start its evasive manoeuvres. However, with only 96 Mk41 launches per destroyer and only 33% comprising SM6 missiles, the two destroyers only carried 66 SM-6 missiles. However, the real limitation was that each ship could only direct 28 missiles at one time. With two missiles aimed at each incoming target with a combined 76% kill ratio, only 22 ultimately hit their targets in the most vulnerable phase of their attack trajectory. That left 278. The DF-ZF (designated by the Pentagon as the WU-14) hypersonic glide warheads detached from their mother missiles that flew at Mach 10 (12,500ft per second) towards the cluster of ships whilst sharing targeting data to ensure they maximised their destructive capability across the fleet.

Flying at 45,000ft, the F35s started acquiring the incoming hypersonic warheads as 58 of the shorter-range ABM SM3 block III missiles of the USS destroyers, and the 60 Sea Viper Aster 30 B1NT from the Type 45 destroyers, launched one minute after the SM6 barrage, started slamming into their targets. The SM3 had been fired in pairs at a single warhead and killed a total of 24 targets (a 41% kill ratio) whilst the Sea Vipers hit with an 83% kill ratio, destroying a further 50 warheads.

The F35s then engaged the remaining warheads, with their lasers operating above the clouds where their atmospheric attenuation was low. By the time the hypersonic glide warheads had dropped below the 30,000-ft cloud cover, some 80km from the carrier group, and after losing another 48, they had moved out of effective range of the F35s lasers due to atmospheric distortion.

This left some 156 warheads hurtling towards the carrier and its escorts. They then manoeuvred through a second barrage of shorter-range Aster 30 missiles, which managed to knock out another 41 warheads. This left the 105 warheads to face the barrage of 96 Sea Ceptor close-range missiles, making their intercepts 40km from the Type 26s that launched them. Only 67% of the Sea Ceptors hit the AI-controlled, rapidly weaving DF-ZF missiles. This left 22 hypersonic warheads only seconds from the ships. The last-ditch short-range ship-borne lasers and 40-mm Bofors CIWS engaged in a last-ditch defence and destroyed 10 of the 22 remaining warheads.

However, the remaining 12 hypersonic warheads had been networked with each other and thus selected their targets without any wastage of a double impact. Three hit the carrier. One each hit the five escorts and three hit the support ships. Only one missed when it was hit by a 30-mm round flying over the top of its Type 26 target. Within six minutes of the commencement of Operation *Red Lightning*, the HMS *Prince of Wales* carrier group lay burning, sinking and disabled, with the exception of one Type 26, which was left to pick up those that remained of the fleet from the water.

4.4 CHINA CLAIMS DOMINATION OF THE WESTERN PACIFIC

Across the region a similar fate befell the three other US Navy carrier groups and two other Marine Expeditionary Units. All had been overwhelmed by missile attacks. In one massive coordinated missile strike over 10 minutes, the surface fleets of the PTO enemies of the PLAN had been annihilated in a vastly more destructive strike than Pearl Harbor. Warships at sea or berthed in the harbours of Japan, Vladivostok, Guam and Pearl Harbor had also been struck and destroyed, leaving the seas around China free and clear for Phase 2 of *Red Lightning* – the exodus of the PLAN's blue-water fleets to secure the world's oceans and trade routes. This would isolate enemy nations from their vital resource chains by using a combination of PLAN surface ships with directed long-range missile strikes to secure the western Pacific for China.

5.0
RED LIGHTNING DESCENDS ON THE NORTHERN ATLANTIC

5.1 HMS *QUEEN ELIZABETH* CARRIER BATTLE GROUP: ICELAND–FAROE GAP

Meanwhile, 13,500km across the world, as one of three carrier groups in the north and south Atlantic, one American and the other French, HMS *Queen Elizabeth* carrier battle group was patrolling the Iceland–Faroe Gap.

The longer-range PLAN DF41 missiles flew 2,000km into space on its 9,000km journey, a trajectory that took some 25–30 minutes to reach their targets (US Navy, French and UK warships) in the east and west Atlantic. One extra high-priority PLAN target was Britain's second carrier group, based around HMS *Queen Elizabeth*, which was patrolling south of the Iceland–Faroe Gap with the objective of containing PLAN SSNs and surface ships from sailing south out of the Arctic. Since 2024, PLAN submarines and warships had travelled via the northern passages on the surface and under the ice and had been operating in the North Atlantic. The acceleration of climate change had opened the northern passage for nine months a year, and consequently changed the strategic dynamic in the region.

The incoming DF 41 missiles were targeting a new concept in carrier battle groups, which were being pioneered by the Royal Navy in response to the UK's emergency shipbuilding programme initiated after the annexation of Taiwan. The programme had rivalled that of 1906 onwards in the dreadnought arms' race. Similarly, Britain had sought to build and design a series of new concept warships that would significantly increase its ability to defend its maritime interests. To achieve this Britain harnessed its post-Brexit energy and creativity, impelled by the urgency of imminent war with China, to build a revolutionary fleet of warships. These new ships had been formed into a new carrier group that had only just completed final operational trials a few months before their first deployment, just in time for Operation *Red Lightning*.

5.2 A NEW AND ENHANCED ROYAL NAVY CONCEPT OF THE CARRIER BATTLE GROUP

'Big Lizzy' had just completed a major refit, which included a significant self-defence upgrade in the form of a S1850 SMART-L-EWC ABM radar. Recognising that her radar height was three times greater than that of her escorts, a new air, space and surface command and control centre had been built to take control of the fleet's air and ballistic missile defences. Like her late WWII sister carriers, which were up-gunned to face Japanese suicide attacks, Big Lizzy had been outfitted for protection against air and missile assault. Designers had decided to take advantage of the 65,000-tonne carrier's huge internal volume which allowed her to be modified to carry many hundreds of surface-to-air missiles. This included around 300 Sylver launchers with 250 Aster missiles, 100 Sea Ceptor missiles and 100 Mk 57 launches, allowing the launch of surface-to-surface missiles and super ASROC anti-submarine missiles. Additionally, her close-in defence capability had been supplemented by six high-powered lasers and six 57-mm Bofors CIWSs. As a result, excluding her air wings, the carrier's offensive and self-defence capability was far greater than any carrier that had ever been put to sea, supplemented by an Amazon-like auto-loading capability that allowed her to face mass multi-salvo attacks of the most advanced enemy missiles.

During her last refit, Big Lizzy had had a US-designed electromagnetic aircraft launch system installed that allowed her to launch and recover fixed-winged aircraft, which massively increased her capability to project power, with the addition of squadrons of relatively cheap fixed-winged drones. Consequently, she not only carried the original full complement of 48 F35Bs, half from UK squadrons and half from the US Marine Corps, all of which had been equipped with the new 25MW high-powered air-to-air lasers driven from the lift fan, capable of shooting down hypersonic warheads, but she also carried six of the new global Sea Hawk early-warning drones that used the new quantum radars that could extend the fleet's detection range of both stealthy and hypersonic sea-skimming missiles out to 960km from the carrier. She also operated 36 MQ-9 Sea Reaper drones which had been modified to operate in the ASW role. With a long loiter time and stealthy profile, each Sea Reaper carried the revolutionary photoacoustic airborne sonar system that allowed continuous mapping of the seabed and objects under the surface from the air, using a combination of lasers sensing the surface of the water for the returns from acoustic pulses sent out from the drone.

This allowed huge swathes of ocean to be monitored from the air continuously. In addition they also carried 40 A-size sonobuoys, or 80 G-size sonobuoys, which could be dropped on command up to 800km away to close down the hunt for enemy submarines that could then be targeted by the task force's own submarines or every platform within the fleet, i.e. submarines, Type 26s, Type 55s and their drones, and from the carrier's own Mk41 launchers, all firing super ASROC long-range (100km) missiles which when they hit the water released a homing torpedo that hunted down an enemy submarine. This turned Big Lizzy and her escorts into a powerful submarine-hunting force that emulated the carrier-based U-boat hunting groups of WWII, but with incomparably greater effect.

To make the carrier a harder target for submarines, Big Lizzy had had her propulsion machinery silenced to reduce underwater acoustic noise. This made her less detectable to enemy submarines, but also allowed her to be equipped with a new anti-torpedo system designed to detect and intercept multiple torpedo attacks from any direction and depth.

As a consequence of the carrier's ability to defend herself, her carrier group dispositions were vastly different from that of the HMS *Prince of Wales* carrier group, which allowed her to control a far larger sphere of the oceans. Her liquid and solid supply ships steamed close by. Next came the inner circle of five Type 26 ASW frigates (built to the standards of the heavily armed Canadian variant and equipped with helicopter towed arrays), which were freed from the role of point of defence and operated at a radius of 20–30km from Big Lizzy, in a pentagon formation.

The next layer of defence operating between 100 and 150km from the carrier was provided by the Type 55 *Dominator* cruisers. The lead ship in her class, HMS *Dominator*, was, like her Dreadnought predecessor, a product of an emergency building programme triggered by the annexation of Taiwan. Laid down late in 2021 she took just three years to design and launch, entering service in early 2025 along with four of her sister ships now protecting HMS *Queen Elizabeth*. HMS *Dominator* was the first of a 15-ship class of Royal Navy nuclear-powered warships, using the same reactor developed for the new *Dreadnought*-class SSBNs linked to two pump jet drives. This gave her the ability to sail at a maximum speed of some 38-plus knots indefinitely and stealthily, allowing increased tactical and strategic flexibility when positioning herself on the battlefield. With nuclear power she was independent of resupply for four months, barring fresh food deliveries from a V22 resupply drop.

The class had used innovative 3D techniques to accelerate the design process and had been based on a significantly modified Type 45 destroyer, which also integrated the acoustic stealth capabilities of the Type 26 into an almost fully automated ship. With a crew of only 100 and an air support crew of 55 plus a marine troop attachment of 30 marines, the Dominators could be operated either independently or ideally at a radius of 100km from the carrier as truly multi-role ships. Three such ships could, when stationed around the British Isles, offer a significant national ballistic defence capability against 1,000 incoming enemy missiles.

Displacing 16,600 tonnes, her hull had been scaled up by 40% from a Type 45 and was thus lengthened from 500ft to 700ft, whilst her beam had been expanded by 28ft to 98ft. The superstructure forward of the hangar space had not lengthened, but the extra 40% width had increased her internal volume. The majority of the extra length was used to add a second forward railgun position, and to double the hanger length by some 60ft whilst the other 120ft had been used to lengthen the flight deck to about 240ft by 98ft in width, a landing area that was comparable to that of the 25,300 tonne USS *San Antonio* assault ships and which provided the ability for high-intensity air operations.

Her superstructure including the bridge complex which had been redesigned without the need for a funnel and moulded into one stealthy body, much like the US *Zumwalt*-class destroyers, with only the two radar towers and EM antenna protruding. The radar towers were 40% higher than on the Type 45, considerably enhancing detection ranges for sea-skimming missiles. Her radar stealth signature was similar to the USS *Zumwalt*, but her thermal signature was considerably superior, due to the zero-thermal signature of her nuclear reactor compared to the smoke emissions from traditional funnels.

The hull's increased size had allowed the forward missile battery to be enlarged from 50 to 100 Sylver launch cells, whilst the area with the funnel had been removed, allowing for an additional central missile arsenal, that comprised a further 200 A 50 Sylver cells, totalling 300 Sylver cells, of which 250 carried ABM Aster 30 block INT ABM and 50 carried 200 Sea Ceptors in quad packs. Meanwhile, 100 Mk 41/57 cells were all added amidships and used to house surface-to-surface missiles for land and sea attack missions as well as the new super long-range ASROCs. All these silos had been modified to be automatically reloaded from below, using an Amazon-type all-weather loading system first pioneered on the HMS *Queen Elizabeth*. Thus these ships could be capable of firing some 1,000 missiles in ripples of 500 without resupply. They represented a 20-fold increase in the firepower over previous super destroyers like the Arleigh Burkes, but with considerable capital and running cost reductions.

HMS *Dominator* could engage multiple hypersonic airborne targets at the 250-km outer ring of defence (extended if drone ships acted as launch platforms) using Aster 30s and the new Aster block 1NT missiles. The next ring of defence was provided out to 40–50km by Sea Ceptors, whilst point defence was provided by five Bofors 57-mm gun stations per side, each with a range of 17km and a rate of fire of 220 rounds per minute (each gun could fire 30 rounds in the time it took a hypersonic missile flying at Mach 5 over 15km). These guns fired a Multi-Azimuth Defense Fast Intercept Round Engagement System (MAD-FIRES), a rocket-propelled projectile with the precision and accuracy of guided missiles able to alter their flight path in real time to stay on target, together with a capacity to continuously target, track and engage multiple fast-approaching targets simultaneously and re-engage any targets that survive the initial engagement. Additionally, there were three short-range 25MW lasers per side, which, when the weather was clear, allowed for rapid multi-target engagement. With such a high-density point defence system, even if the outer and medium layers of defence had failed, the inner last-ditch later had a very high probability of stopping a 50–100-round hypersonic salvo.

To detect her enemies, HMS *Dominator* deployed a state-of-the-art sensor suit, with an upgraded ABM version of the radar system first deployed on the Type 45 destroyers known as the S1850 SMART-L-EWC ABM radar, able to see out to in excess of 2,000km in the ABM mode, to 700km in the air defence mode and 140km in the counter-stealth mode.

With the greatly enlarged flight deck, HMS *Dominator* was able to accept Chinook helicopters to land and take off for resupply, whilst operating four Merlins with tow arrays for enhanced ASW capabilities. Two new modified V22 Ospreys were equipped with long-range radar systems in addition to a full sub-hunting suit, in addition to a multi-role weapons load of torpedoes and AAW and surface-to-surface missiles. Six shorter-range smaller helicopter drones were also part of the air package.

Below the flight deck, a 120-ft multi-mission dock with a rear drop ramp had been added, allowing for four hyper-stealthy 50-ft superfast trimaran wave-piercing surface drone ships carrying 24 Sylver cells and a towed array sonar. These drone ships would operate out to 150km from the Dominators and provide missile launch platforms that pushed engagement ranges out a further 150km. Last, the Dominators had been built to Type 26 ASW low-acoustic stealth standards, which enabled them to hunt submarines while remaining almost invisible to their sensors and simultaneously allowing the detection of incoming torpedo attacks, which could then be intercepted by anti-torpedoes launched automatically from underwater torpedo tubes. HMS *Dominator* also incorporated the intrinsic sub-hunting capability of Type 26 with its own towed array sonar which was greatly enhanced by the subsea combat systems that interacted with all the information for the sensors of its other platforms.

In addition, HMS *Dominator* was equipped with the first BAE Systems railguns, two of which replaced the Type 45s 4.5-inch deck gun. Railguns had been in development for years and had been the holy grail of weapon development, but their roll-out had been delayed due to the challenges of finding a metal that could conduct the projectiles down the barrel without melting. Only when new quantum computers applied to material design were harnessed could the problem be solved. The result was a weapon that could fire 40 rounds per minute out to a range of 350km at 10 times the speed of sound that in the anti-air modes would then split into 20 MAD-FIRES 57-mm sub-munitions. This allowed engagement of incoming hypersonic glide warheads that supplemented the outer engagement zone, and enhanced area-defence capability for the fleet. This weapon could also be used for shore bombardments or for devastating anti-ship engagements out to 350km.

As such, the Type 55 Dominators were the most powerful and deadly multi-role surface combatants ever to put to sea. It was a ship that could operate alone and yet control large areas of the air and subsea domain out to 800km. Never before had one ship been able to operate independently with such relative combat capabilities. Three such ships could protect a carrier battle group and when interlocked into a formation of 12 other ships in two rings around a central ship the Dominators could control the whole of the northern Atlantic in a radius of 2,000km from a central point in a clear demonstration of distributed lethality that would dominate oceanic combat zones. As such the *Dominator Cruiser*-class was as revolutionary as the Dreadnought had been in its time in 1906. But most importantly it was a clear message that the new Global Britain was prepared to defend itself and its allies and protect the nation's vital maritime supply lines, much as cruisers had once done for the British Empire.

The outer ring of the battle fleet was provided by four batch II *Astute*-class submarines operating as far away as 280km. This class of ship had a lengthened hull of some 100ft with 48 vertical missile silos for surface-to-ship or land attack missiles as well as a section where its four 50-ft remote combat drones could dock. These drones allowed each submarine to control a massive area of ocean. The fifth *Astute*-class submarine operated inside the carrier group, searching, along with its drones, for submarines that had penetrated the outer perimeters. In total, this UK battle fleet represented the most powerful formation of ships to ever put to sea. It was singled out by Chinese maritime intelligence for the largest single concentration of missiles in Operation *Red Lightning*.

5.3 THE BATTLE IS JOINED

The old adage attributable to Graf Helmuth Karl Bernhard von Moltke that 'no plan survives contact with the enemy' once more proved true. The Chinese *Yassen*-class SSN *Fast Blade* had been detected at 03.00 on 8 August 2025 crossing the Sound Surveillance System (SOSUS), a passive sonar system on the seabed running across the Iceland–Faroes chain. Royal Navy submarine command passed information to the carrier group who were tracking the submarine using passive sonobuoys dropped from a Sea Reaper, the location of which was then transmitted via a second Sea Reaper using Translational Acoustic-RF (radio frequency) to HMS *Armageddon* lurking below, who sought to prosecute the target.

Twenty minutes into Operation *Red Lightning*, HMS *Armageddon*'s north-facing drone detected the signature of *Fast Blade* and had closed to within 200m of its pump jet. The drone, christened HMS *Alf*, then tracked its progress undetected for 17 minutes before registering that its vertical missile launch bays were opening, accompanied by the tell-tale signature of a procedure for multiple missile launches. Suddenly, *Fast Blade* fired a torpedo at HMS *Alf*. The *Alf*'s AI programme was swifter than any human crew and so, working within its rules of engagement, the moment it ascertained a hostile launch it fired two torpedoes. The larger one went straight for *Fast Blade* and a second, smaller, more manoeuvrable anti-torpedo torpedo was directed at the incoming torpedo. Both hit and destroyed their targets as the drone bugged out. Two minutes before Operation *Red Lightning* was launched, the HMS *Queen Elizabeth* carrier group was at action stations and ready to receive the enemy.

When the ultra-long-range radar on HMS *Queen Elizabeth* picked up news of the incoming missiles from NORAD, the fleet commander launched 20 F35s to supplement the four already airborne on combat air patrol. The missiles were soon identified as 600 DF41s headed for the fleet. Once more the Sea Viper Aster 30 B1NTs were launched first, but due to the 2,000-km max height of the incoming missiles' trajectory, the Sea Viper Aster 30 B1NT could only intercept the Chinese missiles in their terminal trajectory when they were harder to hit. This time the 130 missiles from the Type 55s were supplemented by a further 100 from Big Lizzy which, with a 60% hit ratio, left some 400 still coming. These were intercepted by the two F35 squadrons. Their high-power lasers lashed out at a staggering rate of fire. With 10 pulses per second, they destroyed 360 missiles during the 30-second engagement. That left only 40 hypersonic warheads to drop below the clouds, 36 of which were intercepted by the Sea Vipers (Aster 30) of the destroyer screen. Only two were left to face the storm of Sea Ceptor missiles from the Type 26s and Big Lizzy at a 40-km range. The Sea Ceptors hit one while HMS *Dominator*'s railguns destroyed the other. So powerful had been the outer layers of the fleet's defences that the close in lasers did not need to be engaged. Post-action analysis suggests that the Chinese barrage would have had to be 196% larger, in other words, some 1,200 incoming missiles, to have had any chance of success in this battle.

Whilst the Type 26 frigates might have needed replenishment once they had used all their tube-loaded missiles, the Type 55s and HMS *Queen Elizabeth* possessed sufficient missiles for two more similar-sized attacks before needing replenishment. The auto-loading on HMS *Queen Elizabeth* and the Type 55s meant the fleet was ready to repel another attack within 10 minutes. The carrier group had proven that with new and more numerous missile supplies it was indeed possible to neutralise the PLAN's hypersonic ship-destroying missiles even when they were fired in large waves. Unfortunately other carrier groups with less self-defence capability did not survive the first wave of *Red Lightning*.

5.4 A TACTICAL VICTORY IN A LOST WAR

The question historians and politicians now know the answer to when analysing WWIII is that if the nations of the PTO had not been so slow to recognise the Chinese threat and to escalate their arms' spending with multiple fleets such as the HMS *Queen Elizabeth* carrier group, WWIII would never have happened. It was, in short, a complete failure of US and PTO deterrence. This blindness to the Chinese threat had started with the post-9/11 obsession with containing Islamic fundamentalism, which eroded US strategic focus on the real threat of China. Then, once Trump had exposed Xi's intentions, the West was further distracted and weakened by the coronavirus pandemic and ensuing financial crisis which left Western economies all but immobilised. The last but worst damage came in the form of stagflation from the end of 2021 onwards, creating immense social eruptions. The double whammy came from low economic growth combined with accelerating input inflation as the prices of commodities were driven ever higher by resource competition between the West and China. The result was negative real economic growth in the West. In comparison, China's economy surged ahead of inflation and maintained real positive growth to become the biggest and most powerful economy in the world by 2024 in real terms. Although based on purchasing power parity, which is a much more accurate gauge of power, China's economy had surpassed America by 2024. This had powered Chinese military expansion to reach parity with America whilst apparently having a much lower expenditure on defence.

The consequence of these series of events was that the West had failed to keep pace with the CCP's investment in its armed forces. Thus, sadly, few PTO battle groups could muster the necessary firepower to survive. The ports and seas of the North Atlantic were littered with burning and sinking ships that had succumbed to the DF-41s. In just 30 minutes, the balance of global power had lurched in favour of China and, like the two world wars before, the aggressor had gained a significant advantage that would be all but impossible to reverse in the bleak days and weeks ahead. Unless, of course, the West regained control of the high ground: space.

6.0
RE-ESTABLISHING CONTROL OF SPACE

US Space Command had devised a tactical battle plan to repopulate space under the assumption that its battle stations, equipped with lasers and sensor satellites, had been lost via attrition to sustained Chinese attack. They had never contemplated losing everything at once to an EMP that also took out Chinese assets.

However, they did have a plan to prevent China from reinforcing its space capability, which the PLAN had not anticipated. This was based around six B21 bombers armed with high-powered lasers operating over China, destroying any missile or rocket that tried to get spaceborne. Two of the six bombers were hit by Operation *Red Lightning* missiles on the ground, but four survived as they were in the air on training missions over Australia. They swiftly commenced a continuous patrol over China, destroying the few that had slipped into orbit and every rocket launch the PLA attempted in the next 48 hours.

Meanwhile, in the UK, three C17s owned by the UK's leading space launch company fired up their engines on Scotland's Prestwick runway. They were all equipped with the Astarius horizontal liquid-fuelled rocket launch system which carried the UK's replacement missile defence system. The moment each C17 reached 30,000ft they deployed their rockets on rollers from the rear doors. The missiles tumbled backwards whilst the C17 compensated to cope with the sudden change in the centre of gravity. Meanwhile, a parachute deployed and the rockets pointed skywards. The chute was then automatically cut away and the rocket motors ignited, sending the rockets and their 1,300kg payload into space. Within 72 hours the missiles' payloads had reached 38,500km in orbit and were positioned geosynchronously above the UK, the northern Atlantic and the South China Sea.

However impressive these missile defences were, they were too late to save the strategic balance of power, which had irrevocably tipped in favour of the CCP and the PLAN.

7.0 THE ENDGAME

7.1 SIBERIA BECOMES CHINESE

During the three days it took the space stations to reach combat orbit, Xi's forces had been hard at work. Operation *Red Wave* had achieved all its objectives in a stunning example of a new form of land lightning warfare that rivalled Hitler's army's blitzkrieg victories of 1940. Within days the PLAN's light airborne forces had secured all their objectives and had been reinforced by the heavy infantry and armoured divisions of the PLA, with relatively little opposition from Russia, which lacked the heavy-lift capability to move their army in the west over the Urals into the east. The prospect of a Russian counter-offensive across the vast spaces of eastern Russia against the large and capable PLAN was considered unviable, forcing Russia to accept the loss of its eastern territories to China.

7.2 THE WORLD'S OCEANS BECOME CLOSED TO THE PTO

At 04.30 on 8 August 2025, exactly 30 minutes after the first lightning barrage was launched, a second barrage of 5,000 missiles had been launched at the largest ships of the non-Chinese merchant fleets. In a stroke, the world's global supply chain went to the bottom of the ocean and nations that were interdependent on trade now stood alone and isolated, with starvation beckoning. Meanwhile, PLAN forces tightened their hold on the oceans and destroyed the few warships that had escaped Operation *Red Lightning*. In so doing, they consolidated control of the oceans from the Red Sea to the western seaboard of America.

By the end of the third day of Operation *Red Lightning*, the PLAN stood astride a world that had completely changed. The majority of the combat had been at sea; there was very little TV footage the public could view except for the CCP propaganda which quickly brought home the magnitude of the disaster and defeat. Naturally, there was public outcry as politicians and military advisors decided what military options were available.

7.3 THE PTO'S OPTIONS TO RESPOND

The possibilities of retaliatory conventional strikes were excluded as the loss of the naval forces in the Pacific precluded such an outcome. Most importantly, the loss of the global merchant fleet to supply the West's nations meant that the West's ability to avoid starvation and rebuild its forces was questionable. Not so for China, who now had a secure and strong resource chain to feed a manufacturing and shipbuilding capability greater than the rest of the world put together.

There was one last option to be considered in the days and weeks following 8 August. Nuclear retaliation. On the dawn of the third day, Xi anticipated this avenue of thought and made it very clear that the use of just one nuclear weapon against China would mean that he would respond with all-out nuclear war and both sides would inevitably be destroyed. Xi then offered a ceasefire and truce. He copied this doctrine from Putin, who from 2016 onwards had expounded this smash, grab and hold policy that took advantage of the breakdown in mutual assured destruction and the weakness of Western leaders' intent.

No-one doubted Xi's intentions. The West's only options were freedom and certain death, or acceptance of the truce. This truce was very similar to one Vichy France had signed with Germany in 1940. Only Britain stood alone and refused to sign the treaty, feeling secure under its space stations and behind its fleet of *Dominator* cruisers that could protect against CCP and PLAN aggression, for a time at least!

7.4 THE WORLD POST-WWIII

In a post-WWI or WWII world, leaders and populations hardened by war might have chosen to call Xi's nuclear bluff. However, both the Western world and Russia chose a truce, relying on hope whilst turning a blind eye to Vichy France's past fate, and made peace with China, ceding control of Siberia, the Pacific and the Indian Ocean to the PLAN. This gave Xi uninhibited control of China's resource chains and supply lines to accelerate its growth and integrate gains.

Thus, it was only a matter of time before, some years later, and after a continued expansion of its armed forces and especially its navy, the CCP emulated the UK *Dominator*-class cruisers and built over 100 of them. With such force the free world could not hope to match, the CCP initiated the second phase of its war of expansion to dominate the world, eradicate the democratic nations and subjugate their populations, as it did when it annexed Hong Kong in 2020, using its control of the oceans to strike when and where it chose.

CONCLUSION

Hopefully this story will awaken in both our leaders and the population the recognition that history is repeating itself with the current rise of China, a very real threat that we all need to both recognise and deter with all our national intentions. Many might not subscribe to the shortness of the 2025 timeframe, but I would point out that the peak of the commodity cycle is due in 2025–27, and that this has historically coincided with previous great conflicts, such as WWI. The next question is, will the PLAN be ready by 2025 to enact such a strike? The 2020 Chinese shift to a five-year plan is very real and took place during the pandemic in 2020. I believe it is the very same plan as the Nazis enacted in 1936 with their four-year plan, part of which has been the stockpiling of resources and the shift to an internally fuelled consumer society, negating the need for Western markets. With the world's greatest manufacturing capability and increased US–China polarisation we will inevitably see a huge acceleration of the arms' race over the next four years.

The big question is: will we in the West and the UK rise to the challenge and see the threat of the CCP for what it is, an existential threat to our very democratic existence, as we cannot mutually exist in the world view of the CCP? If anyone doubts this, they only have to look at the systematic eradication of democracy in Hong Kong to know what future awaits us if we continue to sleepwalk into 2025.

For further information see
***Now or Never: The Global Forecaster UK Strategic Defence Review* 2020.**

https://www.davidmurrin.co.uk/blog-entry/now-or-never-the-global-forecaster-2020-strategic-defence-review-part-1-introduction

DOMINATOR-CLASS CRUISERS

EXPLORING THE CONCEPTS BEHIND THEM, FACT OR FICTION?

In a time when battleships usually took several years to build, the construction and launch in 1906 of HMS *Dreadnought* in less than 12 months was a demonstration of British military intention and industrial might. But most critically, her all big gun design and steam turbines made every ship built before that point obsolete. The geostrategic consequences were enormous as it gave Germany a window to attempt to challenge for control of the world's oceans and accelerated the British-German naval arms' race to astronomical levels. Today we are witnessing a new and fourth great industrial arms' race, catalysed by China's hegemonic ambitions as it seeks to outbuild America and its allies to create a blue-water navy that can dominate the world's oceans. In this similar environment, perhaps it is time to consider the emergence of a new class of *Dominator* cruisers, each able to act independently and to control the space, air, surface and subsea domains out to a radius of 800km against enemy saturation missile attacks and task forces. Three such ships would provide a formidable anti-ballistic missile defence to a carrier group or Britain's island home, whilst 12 ships deployed in an interlocking lattice formation could protect the whole of the Northern Atlantic.

To find out more, join our subscription list online:

https://www.davidmurrin.co.uk/article/the-next-dreadnought-revolution-dominator-class-cruisers

ABOUT GLOBAL FORECASTER

David Murrin is passionately interested in Defence. As a geophysicist, financier, entrepreneur and historian he is also an expert on both the past and future warfare with a unique perspective on our armed forces. He has employed a multi-dimensional approach to assessing our defence capabilities and future imperatives. This has led to *Now or Never: The Global Forecaster UK Strategic Defence Review 2020*, which aims to provide an independent assessment of Britain's defence needs at this critical time in our island history. David invites you to take ownership of our country's future by reading this document and recognising how important Defence will be in preserving our very nation.

Global Forecaster models and predictions are focused on finding deep-seated patterns in history and using them to understand and accurately predict the future in today's turbulent geopolitical dynamics and financial markets. These predictions are based on David's book, *Breaking the Code of History*, which uses a series of unique models to describe human systems and their cyclical behaviour that are applicable to empires, nations, military organisations and companies. One of the core models is the five-stage roadmap which has had a remarkable track record of predicting events over the past two decades. Details of the models and predictions can be found at **www.globalforecaster.co.uk**

One of the first Global Forecaster predictions in 2003 was that the war against Islamic fundamentalism was not the main threat to Britain and the West, but rather it was the rise of China and its hegemonic challenge to America, in other words, the onset of strategic competition, trade wars and a new arms' race in the decades ahead, that would come to a dangerous head in 2025–27 with the risk of World War III. Over 18 years later the prediction that China would march on the road to war looks frighteningly prescient.

www.globalforecaster.co.uk
www.davidmurrin.co.uk/breaking-the-code-of-history

GLOSSARY

AAW anti-air warfare

ABM anti-ballistic missile

ASROC US anti-submarine rocket designed to fire a torpedo at 10-km range. A super ASROC is a theoretical longer-range version.

Aster 15 missile European short-to-medium range out to 40km surface to air missile

Aster 30 Block 30 ABM Block INT The ABM upgrade to the Aster 30

Aster 30 missile European short-to-long range surface to air missile well over 100km

ASW anti-submarine warfare

CCP Chinese Communist Party

CIWS close-in weapon system, designed for last-ditch ship defence

DF-21 short-range PLAN ballistic missile with a range of 2,150km

DF-26 medium-range PLAN ballistic missile with a range of 5,000km

DF-41 long-range PLAN ballistic missile with a range of 15,000km

DF-ZF hypersonic ship killing warhead delivered by DF-21s, DF-26s and DF-41s. US designation WU-14.

EMP electromagnetic pulse

F-35B US multi-role vertical take-off and landing fighter with a 25MW lift fan that can power a laser. Packed full of sensors and connected to multiple air and surface platforms.

IP intellectual property

MAD-FIRES Multi Azimuth Defence Fast Intercept Round Engagement system 57mm round. These are new rounds in development that with rocket thrusters act like mini highly manoeuvrable missiles.

Mk41 VLS current US vertical launch systems able to fire all US types of missiles.

Mk57 VLS the most recent version of VLSs deployed on the *Zumwalt*-class ships. They are larger cells and able to be deployed on ships in multiple locations.

PLA People's Liberation Army

PLAN People's Liberation Army Navy

PTO Pacific Treaty Organization – a projected official manifestation of the current loose alliance known as the Quad (US, Japan, Australia and India), with the UK soon to join.

Sea Ceptor missile the Royal Navy's short-to-medium-range missile

Sea Vipers The Royal Navy's designation for the Aster 15 and Aster 30 missiles. Highly manoeuvrable with a PK hit ratio of 1:1.

Smart-L EWC early-warning ABM radar state-of-the-art super long-range air defence and ABM radars deployed on UK warships

SM3 medium-range US anti-ballistic missile

SM6 long-range US anti-ballistic missile

SOSUS sound underwater surveillance system first deployed in the Cold War across the Iceland–Faroe Gap and around the US coast

SSBN submersible ship ballistic missile-carrying nuclear submarine. Known as 'Boomers', they carry a nation's nuclear deterrent.

SSN submersible ship nuclear submarine. These are attack subs that hunt other submarines and surface ships and can attack land targets with cruise missiles.

Sylver vertical launch cells equipping Type 45s

Type 26 Royal Navy anti-submarine frigate

Type 45 Royal Navy air defence destroyer

VLS vertical launch system

PICTURE CREDITS

Page 6: HMS *Defender* using her Sea Viper air missile defence system. Whilst currently a world-leading air defence destroyer, the Type 45 needs to be upgraded to counter ballistic missile threats by radar and system upgrades and the integration of Mark 41 launches able to fire the US SM6 anti-ballistic missiles (ABMs). Additionally more ABM-capable Type 45s will have to be built, as with the advent of Chinese DF21 and DF26 missiles in future both warships and merchant ships will be vulnerable to long-range attack. *Credit: UK MoD © Crown copyright 2020.*

Page 41 (top): HMS *Dreadnought c.1906. Source: U.S. Naval Historical Center.*

Page 41 (bottom): Jacksonville, Florida (25 October 2016): The guided-missile destroyer USS *Zumwalt* transits Naval Station Mayport Harbor on its way into port. *Courtesy of US Navy/Petty Officer 2nd Class Timothy Schumaker.*

INDEX